Dinner for Lit

written by Jay Dale

illustrated by Amanda Gulliver

"Look at me!" shouted Little Ted.

"I am playing on my swing."

The swing went up and down.
Little Ted looked happy.

"Little Ted!" shouted Grandpa Ted.

"Come in.

Come in to me."

"Oh, Grandpa Ted," said Little Ted.
"I am playing on my swing.
I am happy on my swing."

9

"Little Ted," said Grandpa Ted.

"Come in.

Come in to me!

I am cooking dinner for you."

11

"Oh!" said Little Ted.

"Here I come."

"Thank you, Grandpa Ted,"
said Little Ted.
"This dinner looks good.
It looks good to eat."

"Here I come," said Grandpa Ted.

"I am hungry, too!"